Haiku Hike

Written and illustrated by
the 4th grade students at
St. Mary's Catholic School
in Mansfield, MA

Scholastic Inc.
New York Toronto London Auckland Sydney
Mexico City New Delhi Hong Kong

To everyone who supported us in the making of this book, especially Mrs. Panicci, our administrative assistant, and Mrs. Benson, our art teacher.

Copyright © 2005 by Scholastic Inc
Scholastic and associated logos are trademarks and/or registered trademarks of Scholastic Inc

ISBN: 0-439-82253-X

12 11 10 9 8 7 6 5 4 3 2 1

Book Design by Heather Jansen
Cover Design by Bill Henderson

Printed and bound in the U.S.A.

First Printing, June 2005

"I'm bored."

"So am I."

"I have an idea. We can play ball."

"No thanks."

"Um, what about tag?"

"No."

"It's a beautiful day, let's go for a hike."

"Okay, I'll pack up the equipment."

I'm bored.

"The camera is right here on the counter. Make sure you pack it. Then we can take pictures of the remarkable things we see."

"Have we got everything? Water bottles?"

"Check."

"Notebook and pen?"

"Check."

"Binoculars?"

"Check."

"Camera?"

"C'mon, let's go!" Everything's packed up!"

"Oh my goodness, what gorgeous scenery! Let's take some pictures...

...so we will remember the beautiful things we see on this hike."

I have an idea! As long as we have a notebook and pen, we can use haiku!"

"Hi-what?"

"Haiku. It's a form of Japanese poetry that captures a moment in time."

"I get it. It's kind of like a picture... with words!"

"Exactly! Haiku traditionally has three lines of poetry. The tricky part is that the lines have to have five syllables, then seven syllables, then five syllables again."

"Oh yeah, and you need to put in a seasonal word or phrase called kigo."

"Huh?"

"It's easy. Close your eyes and try to guess the season I'm thinking about...flowers, budding trees, raindrops."

"Spring! You're right, that is easy. So I'd need to include at least one seasonal word to write a good haiku?"

You've got it! Now, let's go on a haiku hike!"

"Look at that waterfall!"
Let's write a haiku about it!"

Loud rushing waters
tripping, splashing into mist;
furious rapids.

Field Notes

* Waterfalls form when streams pass over layers of hard rock and fall over unsupported drops.

* Erosion occurs as the water wears away at rock and soil as it flows.

* Angel Falls in Venezuela is the tallest waterfall in the world. It falls 3,212 feet.

"I wonder how old this oak tree is."

Crisp leaves glistening, purple acorns bursting out; the mighty white oak.

Field Notes

* White oaks have short trunks, but can grow to be 60 to 80 feet tall.

* These trees can be found from Maine to northern Florida, and in several other states.

*The bark of the white oak is often up to 2 inches thick.

* Some white oaks have lived for 800 years!

"I think I hear spring peepers."

Spring peepers sing songs
of a million jingle bells,
then they fade away.

Field Notes

*Spring peepers are found in ponds and swamps in the woodlands of eastern Canada and the U.S.

* Each tiny, brown frog has an X-shaped symbol on its back.

* When many peepers trill together, they sound like bells ringing.

"Watch your step! Don't crush the trillium!"

Trillium in spring,
purple petals in the sun.
You see it blossom.

Field Notes

* Trillium is a wildflower that blooms in spring between April and June.

* It can grow from 8 to 16 inches tall.

* The flower is usually red or purple and has a very powerful, unpleasant odor.

"Did that tree just move?"

A tree? A moose? Which?
Crooked antlers? Thick branches?
Clumsy movement - moose!

Field Notes

* The moose is the largest member of the deer family.

* Moose are found mostly in the northern U.S., Alaska, and Canada.

* Some moose weigh as much as 1,800 pounds!

"Wow! There are so many dragonflies!"

Little dragonflies
waiting for the wind to come
so they can fly high.

Field Notes

* Dragonflies have existed since the time of the dinosaurs.

* Baby dragonflies live in water and are called nymphs.

*When they are ready to fly, dragonflies twitch and flicker their wings in order to dry them.

"Hear that tapping in the tree? That's a downy woodpecker."

Green leaves everywhere;
small, black, downy woodpecker
hiding from the sun.

Field Notes

* Downy woodpeckers are only 6 1/2 to 7 inches long.

* They peck at hard surfaces to mark their territory.

*These birds lay 3 to 6 eggs in the spring.

*The male is sometimes called the hairy woodpecker.

"Wow! These haiku 'pictures' will help us to remember this hike forever."

"We should plan another haiku hike really soon. Of course, next time we'll be sure to bring..."

...a notebook and pen!"

Go on your own haiku hike! Find a scene that you really like. Instead of taking a picture with a camera, take one with words!

Here's how to write haiku.
- Try to capture a moment in time.
- Include a *kigo*, or seasonal word or phrase.
- Write 3 lines of poetry following this pattern:

1st line = 5 syllables
2nd line = 7 syllables
3rd line = 5 syllables

Have fun on your own haiku hike!

Kids Are Authors®
Books written by children for children

The Kids Are Authors® Competition was established in 1986 to encourage children to read and to become involved in the creative process of writing. Since then, thousands of children have written and illustrated books as participants in the Kids Are Authors® Competition. The winning books in the annual competition are published by Scholastic Inc. and are distributed by Scholastic Book Fairs throughout the United States.

For more information:
Kids Are Authors®
1080 Greenwood Blvd.
Lake Mary, FL 32746

Or visit our web site at:
www.scholastic.com/kidsareauthors